The Golds ___*move*___ to a new house.

(move)     mouth     moon

The woman _____ a book.

reads          rains          doll

Carmen reads a _____ to Manuel.

ring          story          new

She got the book at the _____ .

bite          library          went

"You look sad," said Jean when she saw Willy in the park reading a book.

"I don't like the beginning of this book I am reading," said Willy, and he put the book down on the grass. "It looks like a bear is about to eat the little boy."

"It's O.K." said Jean. "I have read that book before. It's a good story. The boy and the baby bear will become friends."

Willy began to look happy.

"Come on!" said Jean, taking Willy's hand. "Let's go to the library, and I will get a book out, too. Then we can sit in the park and read."

---

What will the children do?    They will ___go to the___

___library.___

go to the zoo            play in the park            (go to the library)

What is Willy's book about?    It is about _____

_____.

a father bear            a baby bear            a sad girl

Mrs. Goldman has to take a book back to the library. When she leaves the house the sky is blue, but as she drives to the library it clouds up.

As Mrs. Goldman parks her car at the library, it rains and rains. "Oh, no!" she says. "What can I do so the book won't get wet?" She doesn't have a raincoat. Then she sees her handbag. It's so big she can put the book into it. She runs into the library.

"You are so wet you look like you went swimming," says the man in the library as Mrs. Goldman walks in.

Mrs. Goldman laughs. "But my library book didn't go swimming with me!" She takes the book out of her handbag and puts it on the desk.

---

What is the story about?

The raincoat was too big.

The woman went swimming.

(The woman got wet in the rain.)

The woman got wet in the rain.

"Oh, books make me so happy," said Mr. Green as he drove home from the bookstore and the library with two big boxes of new books to read. When he got home he put the new books out on the rug to look at.

He had books about fixing cars and trucks, and about making cakes, pizza, and egg rolls. Mr. Green got books about people and animals, too — big books and little books.

Then Mrs. Green came in and saw all the books on the rug. "Let's go to the movies," she said. "Blue Moon is playing."

"No," said Mr. Green, "I don't want to see the movie. I got that book at the library today and I want to read it before I see the movie."

---

Mr. Green got many new books.

The books are about:

1. _animals_
2. _making pizza_
3. _fixing cars_
4. _people_

animals          fixing cars
bookstores       fixing rugs
making pizza     boxes
coloring books   people

_____

The horse pulls a _____ .

book      wagon      sink

_____

The _____ goes fast.

library      train      them

_____

The bus is _____ .

sky      story      slow

_____

The children _____ the sled.

pull      dish      milk

"My wagon is big, and yours isn't," the big boy says, looking down at the little boy.

"So what," says the little boy. "I like my wagon."

"My wagon is red, and yours isn't," the big boy says.

"So what," says the little boy. "I like my wagon."

"My wagon is fast, and I can pull it to the tree first," the big boy says, and he takes off, pulling his big red wagon as fast as he can. He pulls the wagon so fast that it gets away and hits a big tree. The big boy is mad.

Then the little boy begins to walk away, pulling his little blue wagon. "I like my wagon," he says.

---

What color is the little boy's wagon?     The little boy's wagon is  ____

_____ .

red                              blue                              gold


What does the red wagon hit?     The red wagon hits the  _____

_____ .

tree                          big boy                          blue wagon

As the train begins to move, Penny puts her nose up to the window and looks out. She wants to see all she can on her first train ride.

The train is slow at first, as it leaves the tall buildings and sidewalks and takes Penny out to grassy hills and a big, blue sky. Then the train begins to go fast.

Penny sits up. She looks out at two horses. The horses are running fast, too. The train moves by the horses. As the train rocks her to sleep, Penny sees herself riding the horse, running as fast as the train.

What is the story about?

The toy train is a runaway.

Penny trains an ape.

Penny falls asleep.

Mr. and Mrs. Pan have many animals. They have ten goldfish, six fuzzy white kittens, two dogs, and a yellow bird in their little house.

"We have too many animals," says Mr. Pan. "Let's give one or two away."

"Oh no!" says Mrs. Pan. "Let's move to a big house with a yard so we can get a horse, too."

---

The Pans have many animals.

They have:

1. _____

2. _____

3. _____

4. _____

white ducks          dogs

horses               goldfish

white kittens        a yellow bird

gray kittens         a bluebird

_____

The bread is in the  _____ .

kitchen      fast      did

_____

Mother works at her  _____ .

read      gas      job

_____

Carlos plays in the  _____ .

pull      yard      slow

_____

Carmen sits on the horse's  _____ .

train      back      book

Pat is babysitting for Mrs. Black's little girl. The little girl jumps up on Pat. "Can you give me a horsey ride?"

"O.K.," laughs Pat, and she sits down so the girl can get up on her back.

"Take me out in the yard and give me a fast ride!" says the girl, and she gives Pat a little kick.

Pat runs fast in the yard. "Get up, Horsey!" says the little girl, and she kicks Pat again. But then Pat begins to slow down.

"Your horsey rides are too slow," says the little girl, and she gets down. "Can you pull me fast in the wagon?"

"No," says Pat, sitting down on the grass. "This horsey is tired out — and doesn't like being kicked!"

_____

What did Pat do?    She  _____

_____  .

sat up                    pulled a wagon                    got tired

What did the little girl like?    She liked  _____

_____  .

slow rides                    fast rides                    tired horses

10

Blacky the cat wants to go to sleep. She is about to fall asleep under the car when Father says, "Look out, Blacky! I have to drive to work!"

Blacky runs to the backyard. She is about to fall asleep next to the wagon when Andy says, "Look out, Blacky! I want to pull the wagon."

Then Blacky runs into the kitchen. She is about to fall asleep under the kitchen table when Mother says, "Look out, Blacky! I have a job to do!"

Blacky runs into Willy's room. Willy is about to go to bed. He pats the bed and says, "Blacky, will you sleep next to me?"

Blacky jumps up on the bed. She is happy she can go to sleep — and next to Willy, too.

---

What is the story about?

    The baby doesn't want to sleep.

    Blacky can sleep with Willy.

    Blacky can sleep on the rug.

When Andy's father got fired from his job, he began to make bread — lots of it. He made brown bread and white bread and bread with little bits of orange in it. He made cakes, cupcakes, and hot dog rolls, too.

Andy was helping his father take the brown bread out of the bread pan. He took a bite before he put the bread away. "This is good, Dad," he said. "Making bread can be your new job."

___

Dad made lots of bread.

He made:

1. _____
2. _____
3. _____
4. _____

yellow bread     brown bread

egg rolls     cupcakes

pancakes     white bread

bread pans     hot dog rolls

_____

The horse is _____ .

slow        do        kitchen

_____

Yo eats _____ with jam.

yard        read        bread

_____

Father is going to _____ .

woman        work        wagon

_____

Manuel is reading a _____ .

bread        book        back

The woman is driving to work. Her job is fixing cars and trucks. She sees a car slow down and pull off the road. A man gets out and looks at his car. It won't go.

The woman stops and says, "Can I give you a hand?"

"No," says the man. "Fixing cars isn't women's work."

"Oh, no?" says the woman. "It's <u>my</u> work and I'm a woman!" Then she gets down and looks under the car.

"I can fix this in no time," she says.

The man is surprised, but happy. "Forgive me for saying that," he says.

---

What does the woman fix?    She fixes _____

_____ .

a man's car                  the kitchen table              her car

What is the woman's job?    Her job is _____

_____ .

driving trucks               fixing cars                 making bread

The dog wants to play with Ran Pin and Willy. He wags his tail and jumps up and down.

"We can't play with you," says Willy. "We have a job to do for Mom." He and Ran Pin are carrying boxes into the kitchen from the backyard.

Then one lid falls off a box onto the grass. The dog carries the lid into the kitchen in his mouth. He puts it down and wags his tail at Willy and Ran Pin again.

"You are a big help," says Willy, patting the dog on the head. "When the job is done, we will play with you."

What is the story about?

The dog runs away with a box.

The dog helps the children.

Yo puts the dog in a box.

The baby girl likes to have toys in the tub with her. She gets her toy goldfish and toy truck and carries them to the tub. She takes her toy boat into the tub and puts her little toy doll in it. She is about to get her rocking horse to put in, too, when her mother says, "No, the rocking horse is too big for the tub."

---

The baby puts many toys in the tub.

She puts in:

1. _____

2. _____

3. _____

4. _____

a toy goldfish          a dishpan

a rocking horse         a toy boat

her toy truck           her doll

a toy train             the doll house

_____

The snow is _____ .

job       cold       zoo

_____

Kitty has _____ .

under     mittens     away

_____

The woman _____ .

skates    works    swings

_____

She skates on _____ .

did     chairs     ice

At the library, Manuel sees a book about ice skating. He wants to skate on one foot like the man in the book.

"O.K.," says his mother. "I will take you skating, but take it slow. You have to be good at skating on two feet before you begin skating on one foot."

"This isn't bad," Manuel says when he gets on the ice. "I can do this!" He begins to put up one foot like the man in the book.

Zip! Manuel's feet fall out from under him, and he falls down headfirst on the ice. He is O.K. When he gets up, he says, "It looks like I <u>will</u> have to take it slow."

---

What did Manuel see in the book?   Manuel saw _____

_____ in the book.

an ice skate          a man skating          a library

What did Manuel do on the ice?   Manuel _____

_____ .

fell down          read a book          skated to Mother

When Sun got up, she saw snow outside. "I will dress for playing in the snow," she said. "I will put on these socks so my feet won't get cold. " And she put on her good red socks.

"I will put on this cap so my head won't get cold. " And she put on her new blue cap.

"I will put on these mittens so my hands won't get cold." And she put on her fuzzy gray mittens.

"I will put on this coat so I won't get cold," she said, and out she went to play in the snow.

---

What is the story about?

Sun has blue mittens.

Sun has a fuzzy, red cap.

Sun dresses for the cold.

The children dressed up the snowman they made. They put Dad's cap on its head. Next they put Dad's coat and tie on the snowman.

"We don't want Dad to get cold," said Carmen, and she zipped up his coat and put her mittens on him.

"Yes," said Manuel, "and we want him to have a friend, too, so let's make a snow-woman like Mom."

---

The children dressed a snowman.

They dressed it in:

1. _____
2. _____
3. _____
4. _____

Dad's cap            Mom's necktie
Dad's necktie        Dad's coat
Mom's dress          a raincoat
Mom's coat           mittens

_____

The _____ is gray.

want     head     hammer

_____

Carmen hammers the _____ into the wood.

ice     nail     cold

_____

Sandy steps on the _____ .

skate     wood     wag

_____

The men _____ the house.

build     mitten     boat

Kitty, Will, Mom, and Dad are eating at the kitchen table.

"Dad, can you tell the story about the first time you saw Mom?" asks Kitty.

"Yes," says Dad.

"The first time I saw your mother was on the library steps," says Dad. "She was carrying too many books, and they began to fall. When she stopped to get one book, the next one fell down. I helped her carry her books. Then we went out for pizza and became friends."

---

What did Mom and Dad do after they went to the library?    They went

_____

into the kitchen              to the park                to get pizza

_____

What did Mom carry on the library steps?    Mom carried _____

_____

one book              many books                her pocketbook

Jean and Carlos are building a playhouse in the backyard. They have wood, two hammers, nails, and a saw. Jean is working on the outside of the playhouse, and Carlos is working on the inside.

Jean is nailing wood to the playhouse. She is hammering so fast she forgets about Carlos. Then she hears Carlos from the inside of the playhouse.

"Stop! You are nailing me in!" he says.

What is the story about?

The children build a treehouse.

Jean and Carlos build a playhouse.

Jean hammers in the kitchen.

Ms. Wood is happy when she has a hammer or a saw in her hands. She likes working with wood. She has built a dollhouse and a treehouse for her children to play in, and a doghouse and birdhouse for the animals. She is beginning work on a playhouse.

"Have you built a house for people, too?" asks her friend.

"No," says Ms. Wood, "but I want to."

---

Ms. Wood has built many houses.

She has built a:

1. _____

2. _____

3. _____

4. _____

| | |
|---|---|
| sawhorse | doghouse |
| boathouse | dollhouse |
| birdhouse | hot house |
| treehouse | people's house |

Woody is in his _____ .

room      ask      rake

The _____ is too big.

shoe      hammer      step

The women _____ the room.

nail      paint      park

The kitchen has a _____ .

laugh      will      window

Missy and her mother moved to a new house. Missy liked the outside color of the little yellow house, but she didn't like her room. It had no windows in it.

Missy got cans of green, blue, and brown paint. First she painted green trees, green grass, and a blue sky on one side of her room. Then she painted a window with the brown paint.

Missy's mother came in the room and saw the new paint. "What have you done to your room?" she asked. "It looks so big!"

"I didn't have a window," said Missy, "so I made one!"

---

What color did Missy paint the window?    She painted it _____

_____ .

blue                          green                          brown

What did Missy like?    She liked _____

_____ .

the color yellow              her brown bed              painting Mom

26

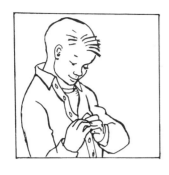

Andy is getting dressed to go to school. He puts on his socks, but he can't find one of his shoes.

He looks out the window of his room and sees the puppy with his shoe in its mouth.

Andy runs out of the house, but he can't find the puppy in the yard. He goes back into his room and finds his shoe on the rug. Then he sees the puppy under the bed wagging his tail.

"You like your funny game, don't you?" says Andy, patting the puppy.

---

What is the story about?

The puppy bites Andy's sock.

Andy's sock is out the window.

The puppy takes Andy's shoe.

Mr. and Mrs. Park have a new baby coming, so they want to move to a new house. They don't have a car, so they get a house next to the bus stop.

It has a living room, a kitchen, and two bedrooms. The house has a playroom and a little backyard with room for swings and a slide.

"This will be a good house for children," says Mr. Park.

---

The Parks find a new house.

It has:

1. _____

2. _____

3. _____

4. _____

a workroom          a library

a backroom          a playroom

two bedrooms        a living room

a backyard          two kitchens

Mr. Goodchild paints the _____ .

window      steps      shoe

The _____ is ripped.

wood      build      sock

The truck is in the _____ .

paint      snow      skate

The man has a cap on his _____ .

head      room      live

Miss Story builds a birdhouse out of wood and paints it red like her house. She makes a window in the birdhouse like the window in her living room. Then she nails the birdhouse in a tree next to her living room window so she can look out at the birds.

When the first bird comes to the house, Miss Story is sitting in her living room. "I like looking out at that bird in the house I made," she says.

But as Miss Story says that, the bird is saying, "I like this house, but I don't like people looking at me when I am eating."

---

What does Miss Story paint?    She paints _____

_____ .

her toy bird                the birdhouse                her window

What does the bird like?    The bird likes _____

_____ .

Miss Story                the house                the living room

30

People were building a new house in the lot next to Ran Pin's building. One day, Ran Pin put on his shoes and socks and went out to look at the men and women working. He didn't see a nail in the lot and stepped on it. The nail went into his shoe, but it didn't get into his foot. Ran Pin asked one man to pull the nail out of his shoe.

"It's good that I had my shoes on," Ran Pin said.

What is the story about?

Ran Pin steps on a nail.

Ran Pin gets a new shoe.

Ran Pin pulls on his sock.

Missy was mad at her mother and father, so she went outside to play in the snow. First she made a snow-man, and then she made a snow-woman. "You can be my new mother and father," she said to her snow-people.

Next Missy built a hideout in the snow. The hideout had two rooms in it, and a window on one side. When the hideout was done, Missy said to the snow-people, "I will come and live with you. Then we can hide from Mom and Dad."

---

Missy played in the snow.

She made a:

1. _____

2. _____

3. _____

4. _____

snow-child          snow-man

hideout             snow-cat

snow-woman          ice box

window              snow-ball

Mrs. Gold parks in the parking _____ .

lot       leg       sled

The car is in the _____ .

store      street      moon

The room has one _____ .

drum      window      door

People _____ in the door.

star      tail      walk

33

Dolly looks out the window of the school bus. Good! Her house is next. She sees her puppy playing in front of the house. Dolly gets her school bag and lunch box. When she looks out the window again, she sees the puppy running beside the bus and wagging his tail.

"Bad dog! Go home!" says Dolly. The dog can see she is mad. He walks home looking sad, his head and tail down.

When the bus stops, Dolly jumps out the door and runs to pat the dog.

"I am happy to see you," she says, "but you can't run in the street!"

_____

What did Dolly carry?    Dolly carried a  _____

_____ .

school bus                school bag                puppy

What did the dog do?    The dog  _____

_____ .

ate lunch                walked home                got on the bus

As Penny is walking home, she sees a horse in the street. The horse is pulling a wagon with a man sitting in it.

"Can I pat your horse?" Penny asks the man.

"Yes," says the man, "but first I'll pull into the next parking lot.

Penny runs to the parking lot, but she slows down before she gets to the horse. She walks up to the horse and pats it on the head.

"Good boy," says Penny.

Then she says to the man, "It is funny to see a horse parked in a parking lot."

---

What is the story about?

    The horse is too slow.

    Penny pats a horse.

    The horse steps on Penny.

Ran Pin built a playhouse out of wood. Then he painted it. He painted the front of the playhouse green, and the back blue. He made the two sides yellow and orange. He painted the windows black, and the door red.

When he was done, Ran Pin had lots of paint all over him. "What got painted, you or the playhouse?" asked Father.

---

Ran Pin painted the playhouse many colors.

He painted the:

1. _____

2. _____

3. _____

4. _____

| front red | windows red |
| front black | door red |
| side yellow | windows black |
| side orange | back green |

_____

Willy eats _____ at home.

walk          lunch          front

_____

He has a _____ of milk.

glass          home          street

_____

The glass of milk _____ .

door          spills          sides

_____

A cat jumps _____ the glass.

out          color          over

The streets and sidewalks are coated with ice. They look like glass. People are all inside, and Sandy doesn't have to go to school today.

"I like this ice," he says.

Sandy wants to play with his cat. As he looks out the back door, he sees the cat jumping up a tree to get away from a big dog. But the tree is too icy, and the cat falls down next to it.

"I don't like that ice!" says Sandy.

The dog is running to the cat, but then he begins to slide on the ice. Zip! He can't stop sliding, and he hits the tree with his nose.

The cat gets away, and runs in the back door to Sandy.

"I like that ice after all!" says Sandy, patting his cat.

---

What does the dog run into?　　The dog runs into the ＿＿＿＿＿

＿＿＿＿＿＿＿＿＿＿＿＿＿＿ .

tree　　　　　　　　　　cat　　　　　　　　　back door

What do the sidewalks look like?　　The sidewalks look like ＿＿＿＿

＿＿＿＿＿＿＿＿＿＿＿＿＿＿ .

waterfalls　　　　　　　glass　　　　　　　ice skates

The girls were going to eat lunch at the park. They saw Woody flying his kite on the hill. "I like kites," said Star. "Let's sit on the hill so we can see Woody fly his kite."

They sat down on the grassy hill and got the food and drinks out of their lunch bag. Woody was running fast and looking up at his kite in the sky. He didn't see that he was heading for the lunch on the grass.

"Look out!" said the girls, but Woody didn't stop in time. He slid on the apples, and fell down on the lunch bag. As he got up, Woody laughed. "I am your lunch!" he said.

What is the story about?

    The girls spilled the drinks.

    Woody was eating lunch.

    The kite fell down.

Sun had lots to drink today. When she got up, she had a glass of orange drink. After playing kickball at school, she drank cold water. At lunch, she had two glasses of milk, and when she got home, she had an ice-cold glass of grape drink, too.

When it was time for dinner she had had so many drinks that she didn't want to eat.

Sun's mother said, "How come you are not eating your pizza? Don't you like it?"

"I do, but I have had so many drinks today that I can't eat a bite," Sun said.

---

Sun had lots to drink:

She drank:

1. _____
2. _____
3. _____
4. _____

hot water            milk

cold water           apple drink

orange drink         waterfall

grape drink          spilled water

_____

The children _____ the dishes.

all        buzz        wash

_____

Father is _____ .

dirty        lamp        drink

_____

The glass is _____ .

drive        cloud        clean

_____

Andy washes with _____ and water.

lunch        soap        over

Mom, Dad, and the children were having hot dogs for lunch. After lunch, Mom and Dad had to go to the front door to see a man.

"Let's do the dishes," Dolly said to Willy. They found the dish soap under the kitchen sink. After putting soap and hot water in the sink, they washed the dishes and began putting them away.

Mom and Dad were happy when they saw what the children had done.

"You did a good job," said Mom.

_____

What did the children find under the sink?     They found  _____

_____ .

soapy water               dirty dishes               dish soap


What did Mom and Dad see?     Mom and Dad saw  _____

_____ .

dirty children               a dishpan               clean dishes

Penny's dog Wags was dirty from rolling in the mud. Penny got him into the tub for a bath, but Wags didn't like baths one bit. He wanted to get away.

When Penny looked away to get the soap, Wags took off fast. He jumped out of the tub, ran out the back door, and hid from Penny.

Penny looked all over for Wags. Then she found him rolling in the mud.

"Oh, no!" yelled Penny, "Not again!"

---

What is the story about?

Wags liked having a bath.

Wags was clean as can be.

Wags ran away from the bath.

Yo is playing outside in the dirt with his toy trucks. He gets dirt all over him — on his hands, his legs, his shoes, his socks, and his blue jeans.

Mom and Dad are inside cleaning the house. When Yo goes inside he gets dirt all over the house. First he gets dirt on the front door and the living room rug, and then he gets the kitchen sink all dirty when he washes his hands.

"Go take a bath!" Dad tells him, when he sees all the dirt.

"O.K.," says Yo, leaving dirt on the steps as he heads up to the bathroom.

Mom stops cleaning and looks at all the dirt.

"Next time let's clean the house <u>after</u> Yo takes a bath, not before!"

---

Yo got dirt all over.

He got dirt on:

1. _____

2. _____

3. _____

4. _____

Mom                the chair

the grass          the sink

the soap           his socks

the rug            the door

_____

Mother _____ the soap.

bug          hid          bad

_____

The _____ is dirty.

water          sidewalk          spill

_____

Pat is doing _____ .

dishes          homework          clean

_____

Father drinks _____ .

dirt          bath          water

The children at Carmen's school are cleaning out their desks today. Carmen's friend, Manuel, is not in school so Carmen says she will clean out his dirty desk for him.

She takes out all the books, the red and blue pens, a fuzzy green mitten, and a lunch bag with an apple in it, and puts them on a chair. She cleans the inside of the desk with soap and water. She puts the pens in a little box, puts the books back, takes the apple out of the bag, and puts the mitten back. Then she cleans the lid of the desk.

When Manuel comes back to school the next day, he looks in his desk. "This can't be my desk," he says. "It's too clean!"

When is Manuel at school?     He is at school _____

_____ .

the next day                today                tonight

What does Carmen clean?     She cleans _____

_____ .

her book bag            Manuel's desk            Manuel's books

Jean was sitting on the back steps drinking a glass of milk. Her cat, Fuzz, was sleeping next to her. When Jean put her glass down on the steps, Fuzz sat up. Jean patted him.

Then they saw two birds walking in the grass. Fuzz jumped off the steps and ran after them. His leg hit the milk glass, and the milk spilled all over the steps.

Jean went inside to get a mop. When she came back out, Fuzz was drinking the spilled milk.

"I didn't have to get a mop, did I?" said Jean.

---

What is the story about?

     The bird spills the milk.

     The cat drinks the milk.

     Jean spills the milk.

When Dad was inside doing the dishes, the children went outside and washed his old car. Carlos washed the front of the car and the tires. Penny cleaned the back.

Manuel worked on the doors and the windows, and Dolly cleaned the inside.

Dad came out of the house and saw the car. "Is this new car in front of the house for me?" he said.

The children laughed. "Thank you for making my car look like new," he said. "You did a good job."

---

The children washed Dad's car.

They cleaned the:

1. _____
2. _____
3. _____
4. _____

rug               windows

new car           doors

tires             house

front             dishes

_____

The  men  _____  wood.

kitten        cold        carry

_____

We  sleep  at  _____ .

bath        spill        night

_____

We  eat  lunch  in  the  _____  time.

door        day        say

_____

The  train  is  _____ .

late        live        lot

Willy wanted to see a football game, so his father took him to one. But the game was at night, and it began after Willy's bedtime. Willy was tired at ten o'clock and fell asleep before the game was over. Dad had to carry him out to the car.

When Willy got up the next day, he said, "Next time I want to go to a daytime game so I can see all of it!"

When was the game?   The game was _____ .

in the day                    at night                    at lunch time

What did Willy do at the game?   Willy _____ .

had fun                    went to sleep                    played football

At Missy's house one night, the clocks stopped, so no one got up on time. When the school bus stopped in front of their house, no one was outside, so it drove away.

Then Missy's mother got up. As she was getting dressed, she heard the time on the radio. She ran into Missy's room.

"Get up fast!" said her mother. "The clocks stopped and we are all late. You missed the bus so I will drive you to school."

---

What is the story about?

　　Missy sleeps on the school bus.

　　Missy runs to the school bus.

　　Missy is late for school.

Baby apes play as their mothers and fathers work. In the daytime, when the mother and father apes are out looking for food, the baby apes roll in the dirt or play patting games with their hands.

When nighttime comes and the mother and father apes are finding trees to sleep in, the baby apes play hiding games or swing from tree to tree.

At bedtime, the baby apes go to sleep beside their mothers. Good night, baby apes!

---

Baby apes play many games.

They:

1. _____
2. _____
3. _____
4. _____

hit drums            build nests

roll in dirt         dig holes

work                 hide

swing in trees       pat hands

The girls play _____ .

jacks      glass      jam

Jack has a _____ .

water      watch      meat

Pat has a _____ .

balloon      bath      bear

Andy eats _____ .

clock      carry      corn

At six o'clock Sandy and his friend Jack are making popcorn. Sandy puts the corn in a pan but forgets to put on a lid. Then they go in the living room and begin watching T.V.

At ten after six, the boys hear the corn popping in the kitchen. "This popcorn is going to be good!" says Jack, as he walks into the kitchen.

Then Sandy hears Jack say, "Oh no!" and runs to see what is going on. The popcorn is popping all over the kitchen!

Jack runs to get a lid, and Sandy cleans up the popcorn. Then the two boys laugh. "I will not forget <u>that</u> again!" says Sandy.

---

When does the corn begin to pop?     The corn begins to pop _____

_____ .

at six o'clock                 at ten after six                 at two o'clock

What does Jack get?     Jack gets the _____

_____ .

lid                                    mop                                    pan

"I will get that balloon!" says the cat, when he sees a balloon in the living room. He puts his front foot out to get it, but the balloon moves away.

"I will get that!" says the cat as he runs up to it again. But his nose hits the balloon, and the balloon moves away fast.

"I will get that balloon! This is making me mad!" says the cat as he gets up on Dad's good chair.

This time he jumps at the balloon and hits it. He hears a loud POP!

The cat looks down at what's left of the balloon. "I got it!" he says.

_____

What is the story about?

    The cat pops the balloon.

    The cat carries the balloon away.

    The balloon pops on the lamp.

Carlos had Woody over for lunch to see his new box kite. They wanted to fly the kite outside after lunch, but at one o'clock it began to rain. Woody was sad and was about to go home.

"It's O.K.," said Carlos. "We can play games inside." He got his toy trucks and cars. The two boys made roads and streets on the rug and made buildings with boxes.

When they got tired of that game, they played jacks. Then they made popcorn. Woody had lots of fun and didn't see when it was time to go home.

---

The boys played inside.

They played with:

1. _____

2. _____

3. _____

4. _____

toy watches          toy cars
a jack-in-the-box    toy trucks
pop-ups              a kite
jacks                boxes

_____

Pat is carrying a _____ .

time          night          radio

_____

Father goes to the _____ .

pop          phone          hear

_____

The boy _____ his dog.

late          calls          corn

_____

We eat _____ at night.

balloon          day          dinner

Sun has a new radio with headphones. She is in the dining room playing the radio with the headphones on.

Ring, ring! Her father gets the phone in the living room. "Sun!" Father calls. "You have a phone call." Dad calls again, but all Sun can hear is the radio.

"I can't find her," says her father into the phone. "You will have to call back."

Then he goes to look for Sun.

What does Sun hear?     Sun hears     _____

the phone            the radio            her father

What does her father do?     Her father     _____

calls Sun            phones Sun            hears Sun

Jack's mother was tired when she came home from work. "I will get dinner tonight," Jack told her.

But Jack didn't want to make dinner, so he looked up the pizza store in the phone book, called them up, and told them he wanted a pizza to feed two.

When the pizza came, Jack took it out of the box and put it on the dining room table. "It's time for dinner!" he called to his mother.

After Jack's mother took her first bite of pizza, she said, "Jack, I like this dinner! You did a good job!"

Jack laughed. "I didn't make this pizza, Mother," he said.

What is the story about?

The pizza isn't hot.

Jack makes a pizza.

Jack calls for a pizza.

Ms. Glassman heard lots of bells one day. First a bell on her clock radio told her it was time to get up, and then a bell in the kitchen rang to tell her that her eggs were done.

As Ms. Glassman was walking to the bus, she heard bells ringing on fire trucks. When she was on the bus, people rang the bell when they wanted the bus to stop to let them off.

The phone rang all day when Ms. Glassman was at work, so she was happy to get home. But as she sat down to eat dinner, her doorbell rang.

When Ms. Glassman got into bed that night, she said, "I will be hearing bells in my sleep tonight!"

---

Ms. Glassman heard many bells.

She heard:

1. _____

2. _____

3. _____

4. _____

a cat bell            the school bell

the phone            a train bell

the doorbell         her clock radio

fire trucks           bees buzzing

Jean rings the _____ .

watch     dinner     doorbell

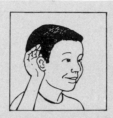

Manuel can _____ Mother calling.

hear     loud     jack

The radio is _____ .

tell     loud     lunch

The _____ tells the time.

clock     call     put

Father took Jack to the car wash. "Roll up the windows," said Father, "so we won't get wet." They sat inside as the car got washed.

Jack liked watching the soapy water go all over the outside of the car. Jets of water washed under the car, too.

The car was clean in no time.

"That car wash did a good job . . . and fast, too!" Jack told Dad. "I can't work that fast when I do it!"

"You're not as fast, but you do as good a job," said Dad.

---

What did Jack like?     Jack liked  _____

_____ .

watching soapy water          getting wet          rolling up the windows

What did Jack do?     Jack  _____

_____ .

rolled up the windows          washed the car          got wet

As Andy was eating dinner with his father and stepmother, they heard a loud pop in the living room.

"It's my balloon," said Andy, "but what made it pop?" He went into the living room to find out.

When he came back, he said, "I put my balloon on the chair, but it fell off and the dog got his teeth into it. The pop was so loud he ran out the door!"

What is the story about?

Andy walked home.

Andy's balloon popped.

Andy ate his dinner.

Mrs. Whitewater was on the radio telling people about her job. Her job was building houses.

"I like working out of doors," she said, "and I like working with wood. Building houses is the first job I've had that lets me do what I like to do. I like working with hammer and nails, too. After I've built the house, I like to paint it. I painted one house red, white, and blue! It's good to be happy about my job."

---

Mrs. Whitewater's job is building houses.

She likes working:

1. _____

2. _____

3. _____

4. _____

with people            with hammers

with wood              with food

out of doors           with paint

with animals           with the radio

_____

Dad says, "Happy _____ ."

bell      Birthday      phone

_____

Dolly says " _____ you."

Their      Radio      Thank

_____

The _____ is fun.

gray      mad      party

_____

Dolly is six _____ old.

yes      years      yo-yo

Ann is two years old. She is little, so her mother lets her take a bath in the kitchen sink. Ann likes it a lot.

"It's fun!" she says. "You get in, too, Mommy!"

Her mother laughs. "I'm too big to sit in the kitchen sink," she tells Ann. "But I can wash my hands in it." She puts her hands in the sink and pats Ann's feet. Ann puts soapy water on her mother's hands.

---

What is Ann doing?     Ann is _____.

taking a bath                    washing the sink                    laughing

How old is Ann?     Ann is _____.

six years old                    too old                    two years old

It was Sandy's birthday. He was ten years old. His father took him for a ride in the car. When they came home, Sandy's friends were hiding in the living room.

Sandy didn't see them at first. He walked in the front door and saw balloons on the windows. Then he heard a loud "Happy Birthday!" as his friends jumped out to surprise him.

In walked Sandy's mother with a big cake. It had red and white icing.

"Thanks!" said Sandy. "What a surprise!"

What is the story about?

Sandy's father forgets his birthday.

Sandy has a surprise party.

Father gives Mother a surprise party.

Mrs. Hill's birthday was on Sunday, but she forgot about it. When she got up in the morning, her children said, "Happy Birthday" to her. When she was driving to work, she heard the man on the radio say, "Happy Birthday to Mrs. Hill from her children."

At work, Mrs. Hill's friends said "Happy Birthday" to her. And when she got home that night, her children had a party for her and all her friends said "Happy Birthday." How many times did Mrs. Hill hear "Happy Birthday"?

---

Mrs. Hill heard "Happy Birthday" many times.

She heard it:

1. _____
2. _____
3. _____
4. _____

in the morning          too late
at night                on T.V.
on the train            on the bus
on the radio            at work

Manuel is eating _____ .

     call       candy       watch

Candy is eating a _____ .

     party       grape       radio

The grapes are _____ .

     purple       told       thank

The dog bites the _____ .

     birth       year       stick

Carmen and Manuel are playing stick ball in the parking lot next to their building. Carmen hits the ball and it goes up over Manuel's head. Manuel runs to get the ball, but he can't catch it.

Then Manuel hits the ball and it goes into Carmen's hands.

"That was a good catch," said Manuel. "You didn't have to run at all. Next time I will hit the ball into the parking lot. You will have to run fast to get it."

---

What does Carmen catch?　Carmen catches _____

the stick　　　　　　　　the ball　　　　　　　　the bat

Where will Manuel hit the ball next time?　Manuel will hit it _____

in the parking lot　　　　into the back yard　　　　in the building

Yo sees a box of grape candy in the breadbox. He takes a bite of it, but he doesn't want Mother to find out what he did. The sticky purple candy gets all over his hands. He washes it off with soap and water so Mother won't see it.

When Mother walks in, she takes one look at him and says, "I see you found the candy."

"How can you tell?" asks Yo, surprised.

"Your mouth and teeth are all purple," says Mother.

---

What is the story about?

Yo finds the candy.

Mother finds the candy.

Father has white teeth.

Woody stops at the candy store window and looks in. Candied apples, rock candy, stick candy, red-hot candy balls. It all looks so good! Too bad his mother won't let him eat candy. She says it's bad for his teeth.

The next day is Woody's birthday. Surprise! His mother gives him a box of candy from the candy store. "How come you let me have candy?" asked Woody.

"I saw you looking at the candy in the store window," said his mother, "and, after all, it _is_ your birthday!"

Woody looks in the box. Candied apples, rock candy, stick candy, red-hot candy balls. It all looks so good!

---

Woody got lots of candy.

He got:

1. _____
2. _____
3. _____
4. _____

| | |
|---|---|
| grape candy | stick candy |
| candied apples | purple candy |
| orange candy | candied popcorn |
| rock candy | red candy balls |

Kitty gets up in the _____ .

morning    teeth    grape

She washes her _____ .

how    face    surprise

She gets her _____ .

catch    purple    brush

She brushes her _____ .

year    hair    stick

"A is for ape, B is for bear . . ." One morning Pat begins reading to Baby Ann from her new animal A-B-C book. But the inside of the book is so dirty Pat can't read it. Ann is sad.

"It's O.K.," says Pat, "The book is made of cloth so all I have to do is wash it off with soap and water."

Ann is happy when she sees the clean book. "Did you give the animals a bath?" she asks.

Pat laughs as she begins reading again. "A is for ape, B is for bear, C is for cat, D is for . . ."

_____

How did Pat clean the book?    Pat cleaned the book with  _____

_____

a brush                  a cloth                  soap and water


When did Pat read to Baby Ann?    Pat read to Baby Ann  _____

_____

at night                in the morning                next year

Candy's mother gave her a doll for her birthday. Mother made the doll out of cloth and painted a face on it. She made little socks and shoes, and lots of brown hair for Candy to brush.

The doll had on a purple dress that Mother had made. It had white stars on it. Candy liked the doll's dress a lot.

"Can you make <u>me</u> a dress to go with my new doll's dress?" asked Candy.

"Yes," said Mother. "I have lots of purple cloth."

What is the story about?

Candy has brown hair.

The doll has a hairbrush.

Mother made Candy a doll.

Candy gets up late this morning. She brushes her teeth, but she forgets to wash her face and brush her hair. She gets dressed so fast that she forgets to put on her socks and tie her shoes. She puts dogfood in her cat's dish, and catfood in her dog's dish. As she is about to take her first bite of an egg, the schoolbus pulls up in front of the house.

Candy puts on her coat fast and runs to catch the bus before it leaves.

"Come back," Dad calls to her, but it is too late. Candy forgets her lunchbox and is getting on the bus with her coat on inside out!

---

Candy is late.

She forgets to:

1. _____

2. _____

3. _____

4. _____

| brush her hair | take her lunchbox |
| brush her teeth | wash her face |
| put on her coat | do her homework |
| put on her socks | eat upside-down cake |

The wash _____ is orange.

catch  after  cloth

The tooth _____ is purple.

brush  birth  bath

Willy's _____ are white.

time  teeth  table

Carlos will _____ the ball.

corn  catch  cloth

Star got a box of sticky candy from her friend. "Don't eat it all today," Star's father told her, "and don't forget to brush your teeth after you eat it." Star put the candy on the kitchen table.

The next morning, the candy was gone. "Don't look at me!" said Star to her father. "I didn't take it!"

Then they found the puppy hiding under the kitchen table. His nose was sticky. Star laughed. "I can wash sticky candy off your face," she said to the puppy, "but how can I brush your teeth?"

_____

What did Star do?    She  _____

ate all the candy          brushed her teeth          found the puppy

What did the puppy do?    The puppy  _____

bit a stick          brushed his teeth          ate the candy

Jean is mad. "I don't like all the work I have to do," she says as she sits on her bed with her doll. "I have to make my bed, brush my teeth, wash my face, and get dressed. Then I have to help wash the dishes and clean the house, too. I want to be a doll. Dolls don't have to do work."

Mom heard Jean and sat down next to her on the bed.

"Dolls don't have jobs to do," she said," but they can't read or go to parties, either. They can't watch movies, play or be happy. And <u>you</u> can!"

---

What is the story about?

Jean washes her doll's face.

Mom makes Jean's bed.

Jean says she has a lot to do.

Purple, purple! Dolly likes the color purple. When she gets up on her birthday morning, she finds a purple box with a purple dress, purple shoes, and purple socks in it.

At her birthday party, she has a cake with purple icing, and cups of purple grape drink. Purple balloons are tied to the chairs in the dining room.

That night, Dolly puts on her purple nighty and gets into her bed. "Thanks for the purple birthday," she says to her mother and father. "Next year, when I am ten years old, if I am tired of purple, can I have a blue birthday?"

---

Dolly had a purple birthday.

She got purple:

1. _____
2. _____
3. _____
4. _____

| | |
|---|---|
| lamp | blue jeans |
| drinks | balloons |
| shoes | food |
| clothespins | mittens |

_____

It is an  _____ .

after          eye          morning

_____

Fish _____ water to live.

cloth          night          need

_____

The door is _____ .

open          face          surprise

_____

The _____ has water in it.

how          first          pool

Manny took Jean to see the fuzzy, new kittens. They were six days old. Jean hadn't seen kittens that little before.

"How come they are sleepwalking?" asked Jean, when she saw the kittens playing with their eyes closed.

"They are not sleepwalking. Kittens don't open their eyes at first. The sun is bad for them then. All the kittens do is eat and sleep and play, and they don't need their eyes for that. They will open them in a day or two."

---

What were the kittens doing?    They were  _____

_____ .

sleeping                    sleepwalking                    playing


When will their eyes be open?    They will be open in  _____

_____ .

two days                    two years                    six days

Kitty is showing her good friend, Patty, how she can swim. She swims on her belly, on her side, and on her back, but she doesn't want to put her head underwater.

Then Kitty hears Patty calling, "Help! Kitty! My new ring fell in the pool! Can you get it?"

Kitty wants to help her friend, so she closes her eyes and puts her face down into the water. She opens her eyes a little bit at a time, sees the ring, kicks her feet, and swims down to get it. She comes back up with the ring in her hand.

"Oh, thank you!" says Patty. "And you don't like putting your head underwater."

"It wasn't so bad after all," says Kitty.

---

What is the story about?

    Kitty doesn't like rings.

    Patty goes swimming.

    Kitty swims underwater.

_____

_____

_____

_____

Manny was going to a dress-up party, so he dressed up like a moonman. He put on white clothes, and put on Dad's green socks over his shoes. He got a brown bag to put over his head. He painted the bag purple with a blue mouth and orange eyes. He cut little openings in the bag to see out of, and put the bag over his head. Then he tied six purple balloons onto the bag.

Manny's father saw how funny he looked. "Do you need a ride to the party?" Dad asked, "or are you going to fly?"

---

Manny dressed up for a party.

He had on:

1. _____
2. _____
3. _____
4. _____

purple socks          good shoes

green socks           orange clothes

purple balloons       white clothes

orange balloons       old shoes

She is Yo's _____ .

sister     street     close

He is Star's _____ .

loud     brush     brother

This is a _____ .

hammer     family     carry

This is Sandy's _____ .

spill     after     grandfather

Pat likes the big, old clock in the dining room at her aunt and uncle's house. It's called a grandfather clock. It's made of wood and has a man's face painted under the hands. If you look at the eyes in the morning, they are open. If you look at them at night, they are closed.

RING! RING! A bell inside the clock tells you that it is two o'clock.

"I like that clock a lot," Pat says to her aunt. "But I'd like to see a grandmother clock with a woman's face on it, too!"

---

What does Pat hear?     She hears _____

_____ .

her uncle                    her grandfather                    the clock

What is painted on the clock?     _____

_____ is painted on the clock.

A woman's face                    A man's face                    A wooden leg

Candy is so happy. She and her family are going to the movies at the drive-in tonight. They will sit in their car and watch the movie. Candy and Will are going to make popcorn ahead of time and take cold cans of grape and orange drink

"Come on! It's late!" calls Mom. They all jump into the car and drive off. The sun is going down as they go in, and the movie is beginning. Dad parks the car in back.

"Oh, no!" says Candy. "I forgot my glasses and I can't see without them."

"I will drive the car up close so you can see," Dad told Candy.

What is the story about?

The movie is about cars.

Candy misses the movie.

Candy forgets her glasses.

Jack's family was moving to a new house. Jack sat on the front steps with his grandfather, watching men carry brown boxes into a big moving truck.

Jack's grandfather told him a story about how <u>his</u> grandmother moved in a wagon train many years ago. "They didn't have trucks back then," said Grandfather. "They had horse-pulled wagons. They put all their tables and beds in the back of the big wagon, and tied chairs on the sides. Many women and girls rode in the back of wagons, but my grandmother liked to sit up front and help her father drive the horses."

"Can I sit up front in the truck when we move, too?" asked Jack.

---

Grandfather's grandmother moved in a wagon.

The wagon carried:

1. _____
2. _____
3. _____
4. _____

| chairs | trucks |
| dogs | people |
| tables | horses |
| brown boxes | beds |

The people are watching a _____ .

close  pool  movie

The children _____ their mittens.

fix  drop  uncle

Aunt Dolly _____ the box.

brother  grand  locks

Uncle Carlos needs an _____ .

umbrella  open  ask

Mother tells her children she will be home late from work. She gives them a key to the building and says, "Lock the door from the inside and don't open it before I get home."

Mother gets home from work at six o'clock. She can't find her key so she has to ring the doorbell.

The children won't open the door when she rings the bell, so she has to go phone the children to ask them to let her in.

"You were good to leave the door locked," she said. "I can go next door to phone you if I have to."

---

When did Mother get home?    Mother got home _____ .

at six o'clock          at four o'clock          in the morning

How did Mother get in?    She _____ .

rang the doorbell          found her key          phoned the children

When Sandy was leaving his grandfather's house, it looked like it was going to rain. The sky was gray.

"Take my umbrella," said Grandfather, "So you won't get wet."

Sandy thanked his grandfather and began walking home. When he saw raindrops on the sidewalk, he opened up the umbrella. Then the rain began to come down like a tub of water spilling from the sky. Sandy heard it hitting the umbrella.

He was happy to have Grandfather's umbrella!

---

What is the story about?

It rained on the umbrella.

Sandy gave Grandfather an umbrella.

Sandy spilled a tub of water.

Miss Gold has lots of keys. She has four keys to her house: two for the front door and two for the back door. She has a key to the building she works in, and she has two keys to her car. She has a key to her uncle's truck, and a key to her mother's back door. If she can't find her keys, she has a little gray box on the table under the window that she puts keys in. She looks there first.

---

Miss Gold has many keys.

She has keys for:

1. _____

2. _____

3. _____

4. _____

| | |
|---|---|
| her car | the store |
| her aunt's truck | the front door |
| the pool house | the back door |
| her work building | the side door |

It is a _____ .

four        open        first

You lock with a _____ .

need        drink        key

She is Jack's _____ .

drop        aunt        eye

One eye is _____ .

sister        closed        umbrella

Willy and his sister were carrying lots of books. They wanted to get them back to the library on time. But it was Sunday morning, so the library was closed.

"The front door is locked," said Willy, "so we can't drop off the books. The library opens again at one o'clock, so we can come back then."

The children were about to go home when Willy's sister saw BOOKS painted over a little opening on the side door.

"That's a 'book drop,' " she said. "We can put the books in there, and we won't have to come back."

---

When were the children at the library?    They were at the library ___

on Sunday night            in the morning            at four o'clock

What did they find?    They found _____

a library book        an opening in the door        a locked store

Penny and her brother, Carlos, rode their bikes to the movies. Penny locked the bikes outside with a bike lock. She pinned the key to her shirt. She didn't see that the pin was not closed.

The children went inside, got a box of popcorn, and sat down. When they were watching the movie, the pin opened and the key fell off.

Penny and Carlos were watching the movie and eating popcorn. When Penny put her hand into the box she pulled out the key.

"How did that get there?" she asked.

"Don't ask me," said Carlos. "I want to watch the movie."

---

What is the story about?

     The popcorn box ripped open.

     The key dropped into the popcorn.

     Carlos opened the bike lock.

# Here are some of the words introduced in this book:

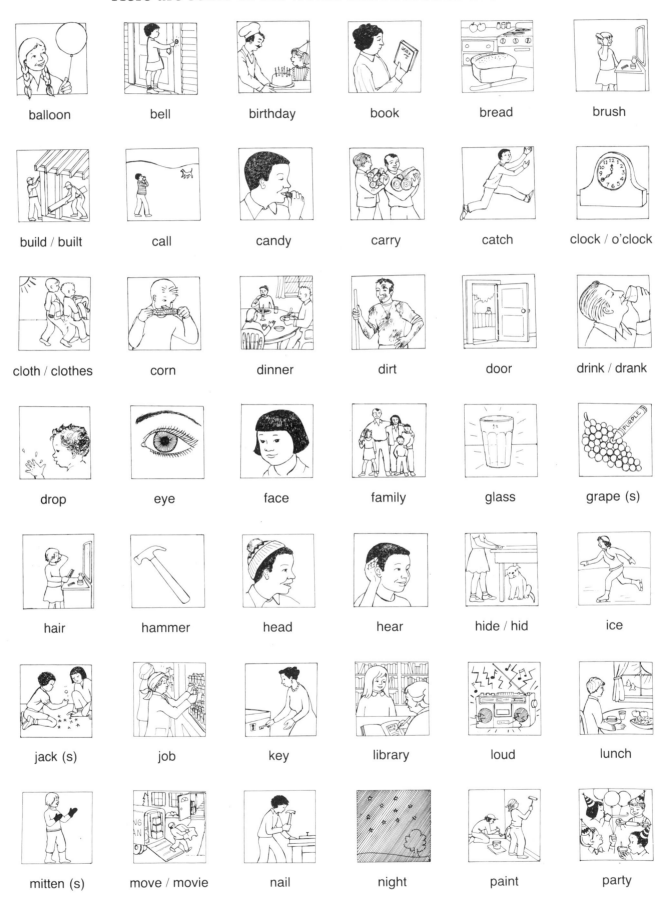

| | | | | | |
|---|---|---|---|---|---|
| balloon | bell | birthday | book | bread | brush |
| build / built | call | candy | carry | catch | clock / o'clock |
| cloth / clothes | corn | dinner | dirt | door | drink / drank |
| drop | eye | face | family | glass | grape (s) |
| hair | hammer | head | hear | hide / hid | ice |
| jack (s) | job | key | library | loud | lunch |
| mitten (s) | move / movie | nail | night | paint | party |